The Fabian Society

The Fabian Society is Britain's leading left of centre think tank and political society, committed to creating the political ideas and policy debates which can shape the future of progressive politics.

With over 300 Fabian MPs, MEPs, Peers, MSPs and AMs, the Society plays an unparalleled role in linking the ability to influence policy debates at the highest level with vigorous grassroots debate among our growing membership of over 7000 people, 70 local branches meeting regularly throughout Britain and a vibrant Young Fabian section organising its own activities. Fabian publications, events and ideas therefore reach and influence a wider audience than those of any comparable think tank. The Society is unique among think tanks in being a thriving, democratically-constituted membership organisation, affiliated to the Labour Party but organisationally and editorially independent.

For over 120 years Fabians have been central to every important renewal and revision of left of centre thinking. The Fabian commitment to open and participatory debate is as important today as ever before as we explore the ideas, politics and policies which will define the next generation of progressive politics in Britain, Europe and around the world. Find out more at **www.fabian-society.org.uk**

GW00775818

i

Fabian Society
11 Dartmouth Street
London SW1H 9BN
www.fabian-society.org.uk

 Fabian ideas

First published July 2004

ISBN 0 7163 0611 5
ISSN 1469 0136

British Library Cataloguing in Publication data.
A catalogue record for this book is available from the British Library.

Printed by Bell & Bain, Glasgow

Contents

iii

About the authors

John Reid is Secretary of State for Health.

Trevor Phillips is Chair of the Commission for Racial Equality. He is a prominent broadcaster and writer, and a former Chair of the Greater London Assembly.

"

Foreword

In this pamphlet, we argue that modern Britain needs a set of public institutions that celebrate the diversity of our society. We do not believe this diversity to be a threat to social harmony. Of course the potential for anger and conflict between different cultures is considerable. Both of us recognise the importance of promoting cultural harmony and being aware of the possibility of sharp conflict between different cultures. Indeed John Reid spent two years as Secretary of State for Northern Ireland, where difference has rarely been celebrated but has become over centuries the cause for sharp conflict. Trevor Phillips spent most of his childhood in Guyana, a country historically riven by ethnic division that has contributed to its crushing poverty. We therefore know what happens when the politics of difference goes badly wrong.

We start with the idea that the NHS is the pride of Britain. It was our pride in 1948 and it is our pride now. We love this institution because it is the best gift that the British people have ever given to themselves. It runs on the values by which many British people would like to live their lives – equity and care. Funded through general taxation it embodies the notion of social democratic citizenship: for each according to their need, from each according to their ability to pay. The beliefs of a few on the far right notwithstanding, the NHS embodies the values of the British people.

And as an institution, it has always been characterised by diversity. A Welshman launched it in the 1940s; its buildings were built by Irish labour in every decade before and since. It has been sustained throughout its life by Caribbean nurses and now works with doctors either born abroad or whose parents were born abroad and with Filipino and Somali nurses all working with the British colleagues of many races.

What the NHS as a living and giving organisation tells us is that all this apparent foreignness, all these different others living and working in our midst, are not others. In fact they are melded together by this British institution into "us". It is a British NHS run within British values of equity and tolerance and it encompasses all of this diversity within its Britishness. Just as in 1948 the NHS showed us the best way to live with each other, so the NHS in 2004 shows how a nation based on hundreds of different cultures can work together for the good of all.

It makes us wonder just what a member of the British National Party sees when they use the NHS. How do they accept the care for their bodies and minds that comes from foreigners who they want to throw out?

This pamphlet argues that despite the wonderful way in which this diverse institution works together, the NHS still fails to serve the diverse population of our country. Medically our bodies and our minds are different. Culture and background make them so. We therefore need an NHS that will in its very essence recognise those differences at the core of its work.

And this is where the issue of diversity and ethnicity is part of an even wider debate about reform of the public services. The new NHS is being fashioned to empower patients. Given greater capacity, people have rights to chose where and when and with whom they are treated. That power of preference will ensure that the NHS will have to listen to the different members of the public expecting to be treated for who they are and not as a generalised member of the public.

But some would argue that this is completely the wrong question for the NHS to answer. Rather, some argue that the NHS should deliver the same health service to everybody. After all, one of the NHS's proudest boasts is that everybody will be treated equally, and this pride stems from the strong conviction that uniform treatment advances the cause of equity.

The belief that the pursuit of equality can be furthered only by uniform treatment, and by treating all people the same, has had particular currency within the politics of race over the last few decades. Indeed, it has often been argued that unless we proceed in this fashion, if we were to argue for difference, there will be greater opportunities for the development of a racist politics. It is this argument, both from the standpoint of the NHS and from the standpoint of black and minority ethnic politics, which this pamphlet challenges.

In terms of health itself, even a moment's thought tells us that if treatment were always uniform, the health of individuals would be deleteriously affected. Each one of us has a different body. There are as many differences as similarities. It is not medically sensible to treat men the same as women. It is not sensible to treat old people in the same way as the young.

In making initial observations and taking the most rudimentary of medical histories, health service professionals base their understanding and interventions on these differences. And they provide a different service to different people.

The same must be true for black and minority ethnic people. These communities have different healthcare needs. Specific cultural factors, as well as genetic characteristics, have an important impact on people's health. Culture strongly impacts upon not only one's experience of pain but also what you can and should do about it. Faith and culture has an even stronger impact upon your attitude to death.

An organisation that fails to recognise these differences in body and environment will not find it easy to improve people's health. Diversity and difference is the key to success here. The point of this pamphlet is not to argue that nurses and doctors don't do this – they do often under the most difficult circumstances. The argument is that the structure of the NHS has not assisted doctors and nurses in making that differentiation. That is why the NHS needs to provide more power for patients to allow them to develop their health and their health service within the basic principle of equity of access.

1 | Introduction

In contrast to the fading mythological history of a homogenous island nation, the British population has always been diverse. Indeed, 2,000 years ago, and before the English settled here, there were black people living here on this island: Roman soldiers from Nubia charged with patrolling Hadrian's Wall. The very nature of Britishness itself has always encompassed diversity. From the outset, Britain has been a multi-ethnic country, made up of distinct peoples and nationalities. And its culture and language reflect that plurality.

The skill of managing diversity is then an historic British characteristic. In recent decades we have displayed that skill as never before. The last 50 years have seen a rapid acceleration in the diversity of the British nation. This diversity has not been the consequence of greater immigration as a proportion of the overall population. It must be said that earlier waves of immigration by the Italians, the Germans, the Norwegians, the Irish and the French probably involved a larger proportion of the nation's existing population coming to Britain. The difference in the last few decades is that the migration has itself been increasingly diverse. The sheer variety of the ethnic groups and nationalities that have chosen to make Britain their home since the Second World War has created a society and culture more diverse than ever before. Of course, some parts of the country have remained insulated from this process of accelerating social and cultural diversity, but in most urban areas there now exists a large number of very different cultures and ethnic groups. However,

The Best Intentions?

Governments have, for too long, perceived such diversity as a problem rather than an opportunity. For 50 years the accelerating diversity of the British nation has been viewed negatively – as a problem to be tackled, rather than as a reality to be celebrated and valued.

The NHS is a living example of that diversity. At your GP's reception, the Irish-born receptionist will take your details before you go through to see the Austrian GP who, after you have tests carried out by the Caribbean nurse, will refer you to hospital. The pathology lab that the tests go to will be staffed by scientists from England, laboratory staff from the Indian sub-continent and managed by a Welsh administrator. At the hospital, the south Indian woman on reception will send you to have an x-ray carried out by Scottish trainee radiographer who will be being taught by a consultant from the Lebanon. You then go to another department to sign on with another receptionist from Eastern Europe, who will ask the Australian nurse to take a urine sample (which will go to the above pathology lab) before you see the Egyptian consultant.

Yet despite the diverse make-up of the institution, the NHS still fails to serve the diverse population of this country. If it did, it would not have allowed consistent experiences of discrimination to exist within its mental health services. It would recognise the need for those services to both help to create safety but also to understand cultural differences. The moment a diverse NHS realised that a much higher proportion of Afro-Caribbean men were being sectioned than their population proportion merited, it would have automatically begun correcting activity. Yet it did not.

Similarly an NHS which recognised the fullness of the diversity of our bodies would have, within a couple of years of migration from southern India, recognised the very much greater likelihood of diabetes occurring from the people coming from that area. Once this had been noticed it would have actively searched out people from those backgrounds and started the preventative work necessary for that disease. Yet for a wide range of reasons the NHS did not. The NHS has diversity inside it, but

6

has not found a way of responding adequately to the diversity in the population its serves.

And society is diverse. Our children's horizons, for example, are broadened by their exposure at an early age to cultures different from their own. This exposure often takes an institutional form – children of all ethnicities participating in their classmates' faith festivals and celebrations, for example. Equally important is children's exposure to different cultures in less structured environments: at play with their ethnically diverse schoolmates, children learn about the world in which they live. And increasingly, for those born in the past three decades or so, who have grown up with diversity as a fact of life, none of these faiths or celebrations are 'foreign' cultures – they all just represent another way of being British.

The principal definition of equity for the NHS concerns access. More specifically, an equitable service is defined as one that offers equal access to health care to individuals in equal need. Put another way, the service or treatment available to individuals should depend only on their need for treatment, and not on factors that are irrelevant to that need. In particular, access to the service should be independent of individuals' socio-economic status, except in so far as this may increase or decrease need.

The second section of this pamphlet explores what we call the paradox about racism in this country – exploring how structural outcomes of discrimination increase when the number of people who are confidently and personally racist goes down. The third section of the pamphlet explores the historical pervasiveness of the belief that uniformity would lead to equality within the healthcare system. The fourth section will explore some of the central policy themes of improvement within the NHS that will we believe lead to a more diverse approach to people's health.

66

2 | The paradox of racism

The important thing about racism is not that individuals who work in organisations that have discriminatory outcomes should beat themselves up. Racist outcomes are very rarely about individuals wanting to hurt other people. That is not the main issue. What matters more is that organisations do not act to produce harmful outcomes, whatever is in their hearts of their staff. What matters is professional practice.

Large organisations – from professional football through to the NHS - do construct outcomes that are discriminatory. Such outcomes are wrong morally, politically and sometimes legally. But we must recognise that they take place only very rarely because individuals are personally racist. They take place, the discrimination continues, because insufficient leadership has been given to changing them.

This is what we have to change. We are sceptical about the wisdom of trying to change racial *attitudes* in a hurry, and we have concerns about what appears to be relentless finger pointing at perceived racists, which may needlessly alienate people, make them defensive and even more resistant to reform.

Of course that does not mean we condone bigotry or fail to confront it where we find it; but we should not be fixated with trying to divine if every trivial gesture might be a sign of secret prejudice. And what is the point? Surely it's simpler and more direct to judge people by what they do, rather than what they might think.

The paradox of racism

In spite of a thousand years of almost continuous immigration, there is a fundamental paradox in Britain. As a society, race discrimination remains a problem, but we do not believe that the British people are growing more racist. Rather, the opposite is true. Every indicator – geography, marriages, language, and social attitude – tells the same story. Most people would agree that, if they look at their daily lives, the situation is improving. However bad it feel sometimes, we need only talk to the *Windrush* generation to realise how far we have come, and how much we owe to their resolution and their struggle. It was not always so, but today, hardly anyone will confess to being a racist.

The paradox is this. How can there be an increase in racial disadvantage when there is no apparent rise in personal racial prejudice despite the efforts of the far right? How can we have more racism without more racists? But that appears to be the case. Year by year, one part of the ethnic and racial divide in many areas of life grows wider. We can see this for example in education, where at GCSE Indian and Chinese children do 25 per cent and 50 per cent better than whites, while African Caribbeans do 40 per cent worse, and Pakistani heritage 30 per cent worse. Or on 'stop and search', where the gap is widening, or in the gulf in university entrance numbers.

Whilst we can never ignore the need to detect and punish acts of bias driven by prejudice, whether conscious or unconscious, this is not the main issue. Logically, eliminating racist bias should be done by educating individuals out of their bad ways, or else simply getting rid of the individuals. However all our experience shows that this is more difficult than it seems:

- Police forces in England and Wales paid for over 130,000 sessions of race awareness and diversity training; and we still get *The Secret Policeman*.
- In an industry where there are massive numbers of wealthy and influential black folk, has it made a major difference? In both English and American football there are many black stars on the

field of play yet there is not much colour in the complexion of the top coaching staff.

■ And do we really believe that the existence of racist teachers accounts for the performance differences between children of different ethnic groups? We do not.

The point we are making about racism is that there is more to this than just a few bad apples. We know this intuitively. Most of the people black Britons meet do not hate them because of their race. So if we are not a nation of racists, how is that we live in a racist society?

It is true that as a society we want to live together harmoniously. We know from all human experience that this is the way we progress, and the way we create safety for our families and ourselves. Divided societies are dangerous, destabilising and violent, and inequality is the greatest single obstacle to integration. But there can be two kinds of reaction to inequality, both of which contribute to social division: minorities who feel left out, that the system is stacked against them; and majorities who feel that small groups are getting the advantages. Reconciling these two is not easy; and in some cases it can seem impossible. We need to combine integration with respect; and if we cannot manage respect, we must at the very least have restraint.

Recently, a Cabinet Office Labour Market report[1] demonstrated clearly that there is an ethnic pay penalty – even when you correct for geography, qualifications and class background. All races, except Indians in particular circumstances, do worse than whites; and African Caribbeans, Pakistani heritage, and Bangladeshi heritage Britons, are less likely to be employed, earn less if they are, and move up the promotion ladder slower.

The same report showed what the Americans would call an "ethnic penalty" in earnings. That is to say, a black or Pakistani heritage Briton with identical qualifications, the same line of work and living in the same town as his former white classmate can expect to earn less than that classmate – for the African Caribbean the gap is about £5000 a year, for the Pakistani Briton £6500.

This is a huge sum over a working lifetime – about a quarter of a million pounds if you are African-Caribbean, nearly £300,000 if you are of Pakistani heritage – and that is before we take inflation into account. This gap might partly explain why it is that these groups in particular find it hard to start up businesses – if you can't save you can't raise capital.

The causes of systemic racial bias

The problem is much greater than the direct prejudice of individuals. Systemic bias accounts, in our view, for 99 per cent of the patterns of racial inequality that we see in British society today. The causes of racial bias are rarely to do with a single action by a single individual. In fact, most encounters which lead to racial bias are never recognised as such by either the victim or the perpetrator.

In an experiment conducted in 1990, by Peter Siegelman and colleagues at the Urban Institute, pairs of testers set out for Chicago-area car dealerships where they used an identical bargaining script, although they remained unaware of the true purpose of the study. The study found that white males were able to negotiate the lowest price for a new car. The same car cost white females $130 more; black women paid $400 more. Amazingly, black men had to settle for a price $1,060 higher than secured by white males.

Further studies suggested that the results were valid nationally. The implications of the study were that in most cases neither the perpetrator nor the victim realised what was happening. A mixture of stereotyping, self-exclusion – there is some suggestion that black customers limited themselves to certain dealers only – and other factors were in operation here. None of the encounters could in themselves be described as racist; but the overall result was consistently biased.

So when minorities complain that the system is stacked against them but can't quite explain how or why that should be so when their friends and colleagues aren't racists, they should not be disbelieved.

The Best Intentions?

We anti-racists have dodged this paradox for most of our lives. Whatever we pretended, we have always tended to focus on individual prejudice – important but not all there is – and failed to attack the system. In short we have been too harsh with our neighbours and our colleagues; and too soft with our government, our institutions and companies.

Our argument here is that when we reveal a pattern of racial bias, we see the cumulative effects of a thousand individual decisions, each of them perfectly respectable and rational by itself – but which taken together produce the effect we call racism. Racism therefore is a collective phenomenon and, like all collective behaviour, we can change it with concerted collective action.

3 | The best of intentions?

The NHS was in many ways a product of the social and political forces unleashed by the Second World War. Britain had been part of the coalition that defeated fascism. The war was both dangerous and difficult, and victory was only guaranteed because British society changed considerably between 1939 and 1945. The failure of previous governments to provide opportunities for the mass of the population had to be rectified because the war made it necessary to utilise each individual's talents. Social cohesion increased dramatically. We were all in it together and the institution that drove us all to victory was not the market, but the state.

The Attlee Government was elected because Labour promised to 'win the peace' in similar fashion. There were very great problems to solve. The only organisation big enough to solve these problems was the same institution that had organised military victory – the nation state. The creation of the NHS was the clearest example of this response. The state would not only raise the necessary revenues by means of general taxation and National Insurance contributions but also deliver healthcare on a national basis. The war had been characterised by equality of sacrifice. Fighting it had been characterised by important institutions such as rationing, where individuals could not legally buy themselves out of the uniformity of provision that provided equality. Nobody liked rationing, but it did provide equality.

The Best Intentions?

The lesson was clear. Only in this way – by providing each citizen with an identical service – could we guarantee equity. Uniformity would generate equity of access. This commitment underpinned the corporate structure of the NHS, and has continued to do so. People still believe in it passionately. However, for at least 30 years there has been compelling evidence of the NHS's failure to generate equitable outcomes.

In 1972, Townsend and Bosanquet observed in their book, *Labour and Inequality*, the NHS' failure in this regard. They attacked the complacency of a political elite who seemed to believe that because we had created a National Health Service, inequalities would disappear. And they considered the first Wilson Government (1964-1970) particularly culpable, insofar as it showed little awareness of the existence of deep inequalities in healthcare. In the next decade, only limited attempts were made to distribute resources differently. In the words of Charles Webster, the leading historian of the NHS:

> "Neither spatial nor client group redistribution proved
> possible to anything like the extent merited by the evidence
> or anticipated by planners….. The economic crisis provided a
> ready excuse, but it is by no means evident that a more
> relaxed public expenditure regime would have yielded
> markedly different results. The more affluent regions and the
> acute specialities were efficient at obstructing any rapid shift
> of resources according to the criteria of spatial equality or in
> the interests of the groups dependent on community care."[2]

Furthermore, the broader political establishment remained complacent about inequalities in healthcare provision. The Royal Commission into the Health Service set up by the Callaghan Government ignored the issue entirely – the index to its report in 1979 contained not one reference to equality or inequality. Labour Governments prior to the present one have not addressed the issue of inequity of access to healthcare because deep in their soul they have believed that the NHS has automatically solved it.

14

The best of intentions?

The Conservative hegemony throughout the 1980s and well into the 1990s ensured that the issue remained literally an academic one until Labour returned to office. But before discussing the current Government's commitment to tackling health inequalities, it is necessary to alight a moment upon the Party's previous failure to address the issue adequately.

Why was this? The answer must be that the Labour Party, and successive Labour Governments, believed in their soul that uniformity of provision was in itself enough to generate equity. Transfixed by the outstanding creation of the Attlee Government, and the consequent mythologising of the NHS, successive Labour Governments were unable to recognise that uniformity did not at a stroke remove all existing health inequalities. However, to critique the idea that uniformity had removed all inequalities was to appear to join the Tories in attacking the welfare state. So Labour continued in election after election to put forward a manifesto that was based, in terms of public services, upon implementing further the 1945 manifesto. This remained the Labour Party's position until the 1997 election.

The evidence, however, was continuing to build that uniformity of provision had not removed all inequalities. Class, race and gender inequalities remained. Continuing inequalities of access to health services were becoming evident from the early 1970s onwards. Over this period, black people were asking for services that met their needs at a level equal to those of others in the community. The election of governments in the 1980s which were unconcerned about the prevalence of inequalities frustrated these demands.

This Labour Government is concerned about such inequalities; what is more, it is determined to tackle them. This has led to a sharp debate within the Labour Party about the role of centralised service delivery vis-à-vis the development of localised services committed to promoting personal choice. For some this has appeared to be a simple left versus right argument. The old left regards itself as the guardian of the post-war settlement. It views any attempt to tackle inequalities by way of decentralisation and the devolution of power to the front line, as in some way rightwing. Since this pamphlet is an attack upon uniformity, some old Labour people will argue against it as rightwing.

What makes it an argument from the left is that we take the values of the 1945 Labour Government – that access to the NHS should be provided on an equitable basis – so seriously that we want to put them into effect. We believe that in the world of the 21st century this can only be achieved if patients are encouraged to play an active role in developing their health and, with the NHS, the healthcare that is right for them. In a phrase that comes from the Wanless report, the public needs to be fully engaged with their health service.

If we wish the public is to be fully engaged in their health, the prerequisite is that NHS must be fully engaged with them, not as an abstract construct called 'the public' but as but as people who have different cultures, faiths and experiences of life and death. Public services do not 'work' without this engagement and in turn engagement will not work unless the service recognises the diversity of who we are.

Our argument is that we now have a very diverse society. This cannot be provided with a health service that is delivered through a belief in uniformity. To obtain equity, a diverse population needs diverse services. Uniformity cannot provide that – and, as we know, it does not.[3]

4 | Diversity in action

While the general position within the NHS may contain inequities, there is a wide variety of examples of really good practice. These examples have in common the recognition that the only way in which services can be successfully delivered is if they are successfully differentiated. And they recognise that communities, languages and genes all play a role which differentiate one health issue from another and demand, from our NHS, quite the opposite of a uniformity of provision.

Towards the beginning of this pamphlet we identified some of the structural problems of the NHS that were likely to create a uniformity of approach to specific black and minority ethnic issues of health. However, we also noted that doctors and nurses worked as best as they could within this system to provide fair services. As we shall see, some of these are based on a very simple and straightforward recognition of how we approach different needs with different services. This is by no means meant to be a definitive list of what is taking place, but a demonstration of what is possible with imagination and commitment.

Diabetes

There are several researched and published studies of interventions for controlling the prevalence of diabetes and for blood glucose control. One has used a pictorial flashcard, which provides one-to-one education for 201 Pakistani patients in Manchester attending a hospital outpatient clinic or diabetic clinics in general practices. This was used instead of the more familiar methods of communications. After six months of using flashcards, the patients' knowledge of their condition was increased in all areas. What you eat and drink can profoundly influence diabetes, therefore knowledge of what may cause harm is important. Over the six months percentage scores for correctly identifying different food values increased from 57 per cent to 71 per cent.

Diabetes has a number of important complications that patients need to recognise. Over the six months, knowledge of one diabetic complication rose from 18 per cent to 78 per cent. Provided with a little knowledge and equipment, people with diabetes can monitor and medicate their own disease. And over the six-month period, self-caring behaviour improved, with 92 per cent of patients doing regular glucose testing at 6 months versus 63 per cent at the start.

This intervention, based upon a simple recognition of different needs to communicate with this group of patients, has empowered Asian diabetics to take control of their diets, learn to monitor and interpret glucose results, and understand the implications of poor glycaemic control for diabetic complications. Pain and distress is diminished, and morbidity improved.

Mental Health

There have been a number of UK-based projects that have attempted to improve access to mental health services for members of minority ethnic groups or to make those services more culturally appropriate. A project in Nottingham Health Action Zone aims to provide mental health services for the Asian community using a community development approach. The particular problems identified included stigma of mental health in the Asian community, the need to address mental health services with a culturally sensitive approach, providing a culturally appropriate service in their mother tongue, improving access to services, and raising awareness on mental health in the Asian community.

The components of the intervention that appear to have been particularly successful are the provision of a culturally appropriate service to

Asian people in their mother tongue in an environment in which they are comfortable. Again these are straightforward principles of efficacy in a health service. People are likely to get better if they understand what is happening and feel comfortable. But in many areas this is not simple. In some small London boroughs, over 150 languages are spoken, with at least as many cultures living there. Matching language and environment to this level of differentiation is very hard. But without it the service will have little or no impact. Mental illness causes distress; not knowing what is happening because of language makes it worse.

Linkworkers

In several areas of health service specific linkworkers have been used. In one Asian Linkworker Programme there was specific work with peri-natal mortality rates and the number of low birth-weight infants in the Asian community. In addition to routine antenatal care, the specific intervention comprised Asian women receiving a minimum of three home visits and two phone calls from an Asian linkworker who spoke their mother tongue, the linkworker's role being to provide basic health education and information and social support. Compared to the control group, who did not have a linkworker, the women in this group had an improved perinatal mortality rate and a lower rate of low birth-weight infants. They also had fewer low birth weight perinatal deaths, required less analgesia during labour, required fewer episiotomies, had shorter labours, were more inclined to breast feed, breast fed for longer, and were more likely to attend for postnatal examination.

Walk-in Centres

Walk-in centres are a new form of primary care, which have been estab-lished to supplement, and not replace, the GP surgery. The prospects for this approach are good. Prior to a new NHS centre being established in Wakefield a study was carried out to find out which groups of people would be most likely to use it. Based on a postal survey of 2,400 people and 27 semi-structured interviews, a walk-in centre would be more attractive to ethnic minorities, young people, and those currently dissatisfied with access. People wanted a range of services, including treatment, and access to doctors as well as nurses.

Language and interpretation

Language is an obvious difference. It matters in all services, but in health services, it matters even more than others. People who are ill or think they are ill are suffering high levels of anxiety. The detail of how they describe their symptoms – 'the pain is there, not there', or 'it starts sharply and then becomes dull for half an hour' – is essential for the healthcare professional in understanding clearly the patient's condition.

All of this is difficult and sensitive interaction. It is very hard for most English patients who speak the language clearly to understand exactly what is happening. So communication is essential for efficient healthcare. There are several ways in which this has been explored.

- **Bilingual healthcare staff**
  The need for interpreter services is diminished by language concordance between health professional and patient. Given the considerable variety of languages spoken by staff within the NHS, it is surprising that this method of addressing language difficulties and of improving access in general is rarely discussed in the literature as it is clearly subject to supply factors and personal choice. The issue of public preferences amongst minority ethnic groups in the field of psychiatry, including that for bilingual staff/workers to interpreters, has been addressed.

  In a study based upon five practices in a London ward all of the GPs were of Asian origin and spoke at least two Asian languages. Unsurprisingly more Punjabi Asian attenders visited their GP when the receptionists were bilingual. The NHS has a considerable resource of different linguistic speakers within its staff, but it does not use them as well as it might.

■ **Remote (telephone) interpreting**

There are many different ways that technology can be used to overcome language difficulties but the most frequently used is telephone (or remote) interpreting. NHS Direct in England is an example of a government-supported telephone health advice service that includes a translating service. There is a wide range of practice from remote interpreting on a shared line, to the innovative use of telephone conferencing technology and several NHS organisations have invested in such technology. For example, the Broadwater Farm Medical Centre and Haringey Community Care Trust have established a hands-free telephone Turkish interpreting service to improve access for the Turkish-speaking Kurdish refugee population to primary care services. This rapid-access remote interpreting service uses BT hands-free conference telephone technology and is available from 9am to 1.30pm via the remote link. The service is being further developed to include a visual link using an ISDN line and tele-medicine technology.

■ **Proximate consecutive interpretation: Bilingual health advocates and other interpreters**

Comprehensive services have been established by some NHS trusts and there are examples of good practice. For example, the City & Hackney Primary Care Trust Advocacy Services (CHAS) provides advocacy and interpreting services to users of primary and community services in its area. There is also an out-of-hours telephone interpreting service provided to GPs. The NHS trained staff speak 12 core languages and are complemented by sessional advocates with 11 languages. The service operates an open referral system. The scheme is internally evaluated through the collection of monthly quantitative data on referral and patient numbers, client ethnicity, unmet requests, and complaints. Qualitative feedback on service delivery is also obtained through annual surveys or focus groups with users and staff.

- ## Interpretation in Accident & Emergency Departments

  Research with patients carried out by MORI in November 2002 showed that the NHS needed to improve communications in A&E with patients from minority ethnic groups. So as part of the programme of work on improving the patient experience of A&E the Government has produced an emergency multilingual phrasebook for A&E staff. A similar tool is already used successfully by ambulance Trusts. This will also form part of the wider information toolkit, which we are developing to offer practical support and guidance to help improve the information that is provided for emergency care patients.

  The multilingual phrasebook, which has been developed in association with the Red Cross, covers the most common medical questions and terms to help first contact staff communicate with patients who do not speak English and make an initial assessment while an interpreter is contacted. It is translated into 36 languages.

  The phrasebook was piloted in several A&E departments and their feedback and comments were incorporated into the final version. One of the pilot sites, Bradford Teaching Hospital, used the phrasebook at the assessment desk where it is important to gain a good understanding of a patient's problem. They felt that other hospitals would benefit from using it at this point in the patient's journey whilst attempting to contact an interpreter. The phrasebook has also been endorsed by the British Association for Emergency Medicine (BAEM).

- ## The use of new information technology: touchscreens

  One project provides access for minority ethnic groups to health information in appropriate languages via touchscreens. This intervention, the 'Three Cities' Project, comprises multi-media touchscreen kiosks offering audio and visual health information in five community languages (English, Mirpuri Punjabi/Urdu, Gujarati, Bengali, and Chinese) in three cities (Nottingham, Sheffield, and Leicester Health Action Zones). The project was developed at grassroots level by inviting the community to become involved in identifying key topics (notably, mental health, cancer, cardiovascular disease, diabetes, nutrition, tuberculosis, cervical screening, smoking cessation, substance/alcohol misuse, and exercise) and the languages. Locations for the kiosks are rotated and include libraries, health and medical centres, neighbourhood centres, and a mosque in minority ethnic communities.

The project has been evaluated through an analysis of computer logs and a questionnaire survey in each city conducted by bilingual interviewers. Of 212 persons interviewed, 65 per cent used telephone audio and understood information and 55 per cent read and listened to information; 211 said that they would recommend the touchscreen to other people and 91 per cent said they would be able to explain how to use it to others. Seventy per cent of interviewees found the system easy to use and a further 27 per cent fairly easy. When comparing the touchscreen with other media, two-thirds of interviewees felt it was better than pamphlets and magazines and 41 per cent better than television or video. This is part of a longer-term evaluation, the investigators concluding from initial evaluation that touchscreens appear to be a suitable medium for making available health information in specific languages. The project is planning to roll out copies of the software on CD to other parts of the NHS where language is an issue and is investigating alternative ways of making the information available, including the internet and digital TV.

- ### The Bengal bridge project
Two years ago, a London pharmacist became concerned that the Bengal population in the area was not accessing mainstream

health services. In general, this community did not speak English and healthcare professionals did not understand their needs and belief models. To address this, the pharmacist, along with the local health authority and a consultant in public health medicine, developed a proposal to provide classroom-style education sessions, which focused on chronic health conditions. Before the project started, translators were employed and links made with other agencies, including diabetes nurses from the local hospital and smoking cessation workers. These links were key to the success of the project.

The patients now understand more about diseases and treatment and are able to manage their conditions. GPs have remarked that many of their patients have given up smoking. Patients and the wider community have also provided valuable feedback.

What is striking about these examples is how simple they are. They address problems of difference head on. If people do not understand the language they need either a different form of representation – such as flash cards – or they need translation services.

All of this work is based upon the simple recognition that detailed cultural and medical communication improves medical outcomes and is not some sort of add-on to the medical process. It may be difficult, but failing to ensure that difference is fully recognised and responded to will mean that the use of resources across the NHS will not be as efficient as it should.

5 | The future: delivering diversity and fairness

The NHS is the greatest gift the British people have ever given to themselves. Individuals and families in London proffer that gift for themselves and for their fellow citizen whether in Burnley, Birmingham or Billingham. And vice versa. Financing the NHS depends upon people paying into this bargain. The only way the transaction can work is if the givers and receivers believe that all will have equal access to their health service when they need it.

Yet, the British people who both gave and received the gift of the NHS in 1948 were different from the British people who give and receive it in 2004. British society is much more diverse ethnically, culturally and socially so it is incumbent upon the NHS to ensure that every community benefits in full measure. People must not just get a fair deal; they must know and feel that they are getting a fair deal.

It is clear that the NHS as an institution does more than distribute health care to the public. It also functions as an exemplar of the degree to which diversity can co-exist with equality and fairness in the Britain of the twenty-first century. To put things boldly, if the NHS is not seen as fair by black and minority ethnic people, then not only will their faith in the broader fairness of the NHS will be eroded but so will their faith in the fairness of British society. And we are in very grave danger of that happening.

So apart from the evidence of the health service failing to recognise the differences that exist between peoples, there is a wider problem of different parts of the public's allegiance to society as a whole. People will go on paying for their NHS if it gives them a good service. If it does not then they will withdraw allegiance. This is true of all groups of the population, however we categorise them – whether they are middle-class people or specific minority ethnic groups.

In other areas of policy this withdrawal of allegiance by black and minority ethnic people has potentially severe consequences. Some 25 per cent of parents of black and minority ethnic pupils in London send their children to private schools. Given the income of black people in London this would represent a much higher proportion of their disposable income than for white people. The Government's emphasis on the importance of raising standards, and the differentiation through faith schools and specialist schools, is aimed at demonstrating that schools funded by the public can achieve high standards for different black and minority ethnic groups. But the truth is, once that allegiance is lost it is difficult to regain.

We are in a position with the NHS where that allegiance is still maintained. But we must never take that for granted. What we suggest in this pamphlet is a recognition that NHS policy and practice to secure that strong allegiance must better acknowledge these differences by black people into the future.

Let us be clear. The NHS is such an important organisation that it is on the back of strong allegiance to the NHS that strong allegiances to society as a whole can be developed and maintained. If communities cannot trust the NHS, with its values of care and equity, to deliver for them, then it raises very tough questions for the rest of society.

The role of choice

Different people enjoy different health and require different health services. But one pre-requisite of a health service sensitive to their individual needs is the building up of NHS capacity. Since 1997 the Labour Government has committed itself to increasing the capacity in the NHS. When Labour came to power, there were not enough doctors, not enough nurses and not enough capacity for all the operations needed. People waiting for 18 months for an operation are not likely to feel that their access to the NHS is fair. So our priority has been to create the capacity. Since 1997 65,000 new nurses and 14,000 new doctors have joined the NHS, and hundreds of thousands of new operations have been undertaken. This extra capacity has only been possible because of both the extra investment paid for by the British people and the reform strategy pursed by the Government.

Without this new capacity, personalising the NHS would be impossible. But now that we are growing the NHS and the investment is secure for the next few years, we have the opportunity to proceed with the individual tailoring of healthcare. In December 2003, the Government published *Building on the Best*, its first paper on personalising the NHS. This paper demonstrated how the NHS could engender a much more personal experience by offering the public much greater choice. But there are those that believe fairness can only be provided by a command-and-control NHS in which the centre makes all decisions about the distribution of resources. Those of this view believe that putting power in the hands of the patients removes the guarantee of equal treatment.

We disagree. All the evidence shows that black and minority ethnic people want the opportunity to chose. Their experience of bureaucracies making decisions for them, of telling them what is best for them, has not delivered them equity. They want the right to play a role and direct, through their preferences, the way in which services are delivered.

Of course, this is not to say that black and minority ethnic people don't have faith in doctors and nurses. Living, as they do, in cultures that respect learning and qualifications, they have great respect for professionals. They want to work *with* those people and want the chance to have a say in their health service.

As the Government recognised in *Building on the Best*, simply offering everyone the same experience of choice will not work. Different people will need different support. People who do not speak the language that their health professionals speak will not find it easy to communicate their choices.

But this is the case at the moment. In all the existing medical interactions communication is one of the main aspects of successful healthcare. What drugs to take, when to take them, how to look after yourself and where to go next – all need very successful communication. One slip in understanding – mistaking 'twice a day' for 'three times a day', or 'carry on as normal going up the stairs' for 'take it easy' – undermines medical efficacy.

But for medicine to be effective, communications must be real and exact. That is why the example of A&E and interpretation is so important. If it is possible to arrange understanding at the difficult and anxious environment of A&E, then it is possible to organise a communications system adequate to support the choice agenda.

As we said in *Building on the Best*, the aim must be for the patient to become the navigator of the system – and as they navigate the system they make those choices for themselves and create in a much more precise way the health service that they feel is better for them.

Another critical issue in achieving a more responsive NHS is the development of better information. The NHS is implementing the biggest IT programme in the world. Over the next few years data will be able to flow between different parts of the NHS with much greater ease and accuracy than ever before. Collectively we will know a great deal more about our health and how our health service works with our health than ever before. To ensure that this provides the clearest understanding of difference, it will be necessary to have much better day-to-day information about ethnicity. It should not be left to special research to have to follow up the issue of cultural difference. It needs to be a part of the day-to-day management of the health service.

Such information would allow primary and secondary care to ensure that its work fully reflects the needs of people within their locality and any separation of the work of the NHS and the needs of specific local populations would need to be explained through this local analysis.

Driving the strategy forward

Our analysis and the examples of good practice we have set out illus-
trate both the problem and the way in which the NHS can respond. But
we need to drive this forward. Earlier in this pamphlet we made much
of the issue that individual people were not racist, but that outcomes
were discriminatory. The leadership of the NHS recognises the moral
case for tackling this and has asked the CRE to assist it in leading
improvement. Every level of leadership needs to look at their organisation and raise questions about the discriminatory nature of the way in
which it works. Some of this can be very simple – a matter of looking
around the room can usually tell you how far you have to go. And the
answer is usually a long way. The Permanent Secretary Sir Nigel Crisp
is giving that leadership, chairing the steering group on diversity
himself, as is the Secretary of State in writing this pamphlet.

The Department of Health has developed a ten-point action plan on
race equality that is both aimed at improving health services and
outcomes for the public and developing the people within the NHS.
This starts by expecting all local delivery plans produced by local
Primary Care Trusts for 2005-2008 to take race equality into account
when commissioning for their local community. To make this effective
we will need to build race equality into the new regime for setting standards within the NHS, ensuring that this is nationally a part of the new
inspection model and locally a part of the performance management
system.

The senior managers both within the Department of Health and the 28
Strategic Health authorities, together with the Modernisation Agency,
must provide practical support to help NHS organisations make service
improvements for people from ethnic minorities. As we can see from the
examples above there are some examples of good practice within the
NHS and these need to be communicated with the rest of the NHS.

Given the importance of culture and language to both health and
ethnicity, it is imperative that fresh approaches to communications are
carried out. Some of the examples of good practice show real imagina-

tion in communication, and recognise that without clear and simple communication medical efficacy is severely compromised. That is why the NHS is going to have to work with a wider set of partners from national and local agencies to promote the health and well being of people from ethnic minorities. We cannot achieve this on our own.

In terms of its staff, the NHS could be described as 'snow-capped', with white people covering the top of the organisation. As we have already said, many tens of thousands of the workforce are black, but insufficient numbers are finding their way to the top of NHS organisations. In other organisations, senior staff mentoring black and minority ethnic staff has had an impact and we expect that all senior leaders in the Department and in the NHS will mentor staff. Equally, to immediately focus their attention, all senior leaders should include in their personal objectives for next year a personal stretch target on race equality. To see whether any of this is working, we need to build systematic processes for tracking the career progression of staff from ethnic minorities.

At every level the audit and action needs to flow – not to expect total change overnight, but to recognise that the direction of change is one way to include more people than it did last year and will do more next year. Leaders know when they are doing this, when they have this firmly in their sights. We all need to do that and stick with it for a long time to come, if we are going to change the reality of the way in which the NHS works.

Diversity of provision

In many spheres – although not in healthcare provision – black and minority ethnic groups have created their own services. In education, in social services and in social housing, black and minority ethnic people have played a role in creating provision that they feel meets their needs because they are involved in their provision.

The Department of Health is currently consulting on what black and minority ethnic communities' involvement in mental health services might mean. This is a sector of the health service that already involves voluntary provision in providing a large and growing proportion of the services. Given the strength of black and minority ethnic cultures in creating voluntary organisations, it should be possible to create some culturally specific diverse solutions.

Lots of arguments and pamphlets have been written about discriminatory practices and in truth not a lot has happened. Different mechanisms and legal frameworks have been argued for at different times that have tried to 'make', 'bully' or 'cajole' institutions to operate in a better way. Knowing the NHS as we do, we are making a different argument.

The NHS believes passionately in equity. It also believes in medical efficacy, helping people get better as quickly as possible. What we are suggesting is taking those values so seriously that we put them into effect for everyone. We believe that the NHS would be affronted by epidemiological information that showed worse outcomes for one group or another. That the NHS would be affronted by any statistical variation in patient satisfaction of services, with people from different minority ethnic groups being differentially satisfied with the NHS.

The NHS has a strong and enduring set of core values. It now needs to recognise that these values can only be realised by recognising difference between people, rather than by pretending our health and our minds and bodies are all the same.

References

1   *Ethnic Minorities and the Labour Market* (Cabinet Office, 2003)

2   *The National Health Service: a political history*, by Charles Webster (Oxford University Press, 1998)

3   One very good additional resource on the evidence on ethnic disparities and examples of good practice, is to be found in the following report – P.J. Aspinall, B.Jacobson. *Ethnic Disparities in Health and Health Care. A focussed review of the Evidence and Examples of Good Practice.* The full report will be available on www.lho.org.uk. We urge people to read this since it provides compelling evidence of the problems that have not been solved by the existing structure of the NHS.

Recent Fabian Publications

A New Social Contract: From targets to rights in public services by Tony Wright and Pauline Ngan

Public service reform is central to the Government's domestic agenda. But the political and policy debates have got stuck. The limits of a target driven approach are becoming increasingly clear, while few voters can follow an often technocratic debate on managerial reform.

This pamphlet suggests an innovative new approach which would turn this reform debate on its head by shifting the focus from the producers to the users of public services. If public services are a contract between the citizen and the state, the terms of that contract need to be made considerably more explicit. A system of Public Service Guarantees – based around the 'three Rs' of user representation, rights and redress – would set out clearly what users can expect from the money we pay for public services, and what we can expect if these expectations are not fulfilled.

This pamphlet seeks to reshape the controversial political debate about consumers and citizens, arguing that taking citizenship seriously should not prevent applying good consumer principles to public services, and that giving more rights to public service users should be central to the Labour's third term policy agenda.

March 2004 ISBN 0 7163 0610 7 £6.95

The Making of Europe's Constitution by Gisela Stuart

Gisela Stuart MP's candid insider's guide to how Europe's draft constitution was written offers a series of radical proposals for engaging the public in EU affairs. Stuart argues we must change the way Britain deals with Europe if we are to contribute fully to the reshaping of European politics.

'Mr Blair should take the advice of Gisela Stuart to reform the way Parliament scrutinises EU decision-making.' *The Independent*

'A fascinating – and courageous – account of the way the constitution was painfully, sometimes secretively, argued, wangled and bullied into its draft form.' *Guardian*

'This pamphlet takes us inside the EU constitution-making process and asks some fundamental questions about it. These have to be faced by all of us, whatever view we take of what is being proposed.' Tony Wright MP, member of the Fabian Executive

December 2003 ISBN 0 7163 0609 3 £6.95

34

Exploding the Migration Myths by Russell King, Nicola Mai and Mirela Dalipaj (Published with Oxfam GB)
By speaking to migrants themselves, this report identifies the real reasons behind economic migration and what drives those who undertake it. It explores an approach that can maximise its benefits for migrants, their country of origin and their host country.
November 2003 ISBN 0 7163 3059 8 £12.95

Progressive Globalisation: Towards an international social democracy by Michael Jacobs, Adam Lent and Kevin Watkins
This pamphlet argues for the management of global capitalism under social democratic principles. Calling for a new coalition to work for progressive globalisation, it sets out the 'four pillars' of a new global system.
September 2003 ISBN 0 7163 0608 5 £6.95

A Better Choice of Choice: Quality of life, consumption, and economic growth by Roger Levett et al
Four of the country's leading sustainable development thinkers and practitioners argue that consumption must be addressed head on as resource productivity is not keeping up with economic growth and challenge all those interested in how public policy contributes to sustainable development and individual and social well-being.
August 2003 ISBN 0 7163 3058 X £9.95

The Future of the Monarchy: The report of the Fabian Commission on the Future of the Monarchy
The first comprehensive bluepriont for Royal reform for over 300 years, this report examines the key roles and functions of the British sovereign and the Royal Family including constitutional powers, the monarch's relationship with the law, the Church of England and the Commonwealth, and how it is organised and financed.
July 2003 ISBN 0 7163 6004 7 £11.95

Communities in Control: Public services and local socialism by Hazel Blears
Transcending consultation and participation, the author looks at how local communities can own, manage, plan, and benefit from public services. Blears calls for new forms of community interest companies and a Citizen Participation Agency to create a new generation of community activists and leaders.
June 2003 ISBN 0 7163 0607 7 £6.95

Wealth's Fair Measure:The reform of inheritance tax by Ruth Patrick and Michael Jacobs
Inheritance tax avoidance has become too easy, making the tax unfair and virtually voluntary. This publication explores how best it could be reformed, and the problems with the current system.
April 2003 ISBN 0 7163 3057 1 £9.95

Commercialisation or Citizenship: Education policy and the future of public services by Colin Crouch
An analysis of private sector involvement in public service, showing how this threatens the citizenship basis of education. Crouch offers a number of proposals for a strategy of modernising public services in a manner which is compatible with the concept of the welfare state as a fundamental component of social citizenship.
March 2003 ISBN 0 7163 0606 9 £6.95

All's well that starts well: Strategy for children's health by Howard Stoate and Bryan Jones
Britain is becoming a chronically unfit society with one in five adults dangerously overweight and the life expectancy of children being less than our own. Stoate offers a range of possible strategies from guidelines on meal planning to tax incentives to fresh produce suppliers.
December 2002 ISBN 0 7163 0604 2 £6.95

Completing the Course: Health to 2010 by Ray Robinson and Anna Dixon
During the Second Term the Fabian Society has held a series of seminars as part of its Health Policy Forum to provide members of the policy community, politicians and opinion formers with the opportunity to debate the key issues in the long term development of health politics and policy in the UK. This pamphlet provides a comprehensive guide to the current reforms and argues that a period of stability is needed to bring about sustainable service improvements, with greater continuity than has been evident over the last decade.
December 2002 ISBN 0 7163 0605 0 £6.95

The Courage of Our Convictions: Why reform of the public services is the route to social justice by Tony Blair
Acknowledging that tension exists between national audits and inspections and local autonomy, Blair argues that this can be overcome and sets out his four principles of reform: national standards, devolved power, professionalism and choice.
September 2002, ISBN 0 7163 0603 4, £6.95

Paying for Progress: A new politics of tax for public spending
The highly influential report of the Fabian Taxation Commission which argues for a new approach to taxation and the public spending it pays for, arguing that the public must be 'reconnected' to taxes and the public services which these finance. Providing key information on the UK tax system, this text examines a series of reforms possible to meet the goals of social inclusion and environmental protection.
November 2000 ISBN 0 7163 6003 9 £9.95

To order any of the above titles please email bookshop@fabian-society.org.uk or ring 020 7227 4900